THE OFFICIAL JUSTIN BIEBER

SECRL

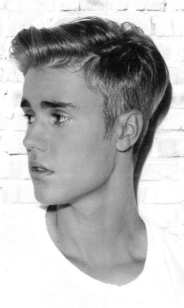

centum

THIS BOOK
BELONGS TO...

ME, MYSELF AND I

Fill in the page with all the brilliant things about what makes you unique and you, totally you!

name

nickname

birthday

age

year born

star sign

home town/city

Snapchat/IG handle

best friend

pets

biggest achievement

proudest moment

most embarrassing moment

best thing about me

Nobody could resist a double-tap on for Justin's pet pooch, Esther.

TICK OR DRAW YOUR SELFIE HERE.

>>>> eye colour
☐ brown ☐ green
☐ blue ☐ hazel

>>>> hair colour
☐ brown ☐ red
☐ blonde ☐ black
☐ strawberry blonde

>>>> face shape
☐ round ☐ long
☐ oval ☐ square
☐ heart-shaped

SHHHHH!

Only my (mum/best friend/sister/brother) knows that I _____

_____

_____

_____

JUSTIN HAS AN OVAL FACE, WHICH IS APPARENTLY THE PERFECT FACE SHAPE AND BEST FOR PULLING OFF LOADS OF DIFFERENT HAIRSTYLES.

BIEBER BASICS

All true Beliebers should know the basic Bieber facts. Read on to discover some simple stats about the boy wonder!

> BEFORE HE WAS FAMOUS, JUSTIN BUSKED ON THE STREETS IN HIS HOME TOWN.

NAME: Justin Drew Bieber

NATIONALITY: Canadian

DOB: 1st March 1994

BORN: London, Ontario, Canada

LOVES: basketball, ice hockey, Italian food, funny YouTube vids and his FANS!

INSTRUMENTS PLAYED: drums, guitar, piano and trumpet

STUDIO ALBUMS RELEASED: 4 so far!

TWITTER MENTIONS: around 60 a second! #GetCloser

> JUSTIN IS A PISCES.

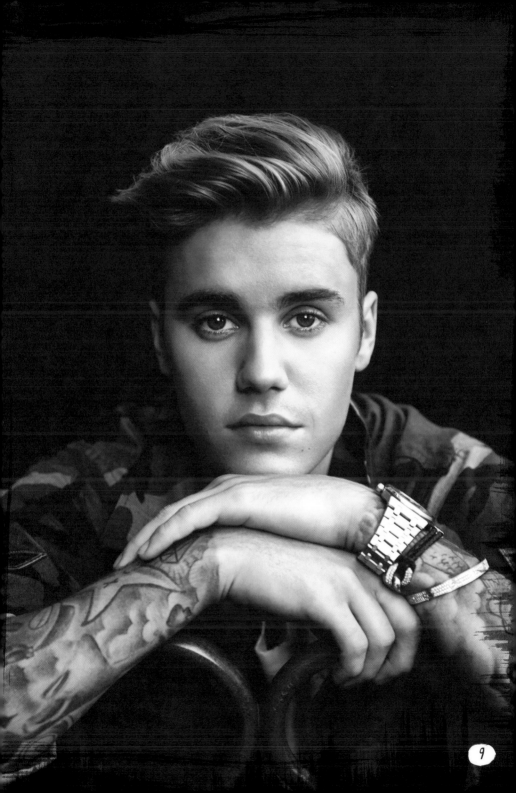

A FEW OF MY FAVOURITE THINGS

Fill in the page with all of your favourite things in life.

MY FAVE...

friend _____

family member _____

film _____

song _____

accessory _____

tv show _____

outfit _____

vlogger _____

choccie bar _____

shop _____

animal _____

sport _____

food _____

drink _____

shoes _____

time of year _____

day of the week _____

How well do you know Justin?

Tick the boxes to show his fave things.

> > > > fave sport

☐ ice hockey   ☐ soccer   ☐ ski-ing

> > > > fave food

☐ sausages   ☐ spag bol   ☐ sprouts

> > > > fave colour

☐ blue   ☐ green   ☐ purple

Answers on page 92

MY TOP 3 FAVE JB SONGS!

1 _____

2 _____

3 _____

FAMILY FUN

Even if your parents, brothers and sisters drive you loopy at times, it's great to have people you can always count on and who'll love you forever!

FILL IN YOUR FAMILY TREE WITH NAMES, PICS OR DOODLES TO SHOW WHO'S WHO IN YOUR FAMILY.

← PIC

← NAME

IF YOUR FAMILY WERE A TV SHOW, WHAT WOULD IT BE?

WHO IN YOUR FAMILY IS THE...

cuddliest _____

loudest _____

happiest _____

messiest _____

funniest _____

chattiest _____

JB LOVES HIS MUM SO MUCH HE HAS HER EYE TATTOOED ON HIS ARM!

SONG SEARCH

Up for a challenge? See how quickly you can find all these brilliant Bieber hits in the wordsearch grid.

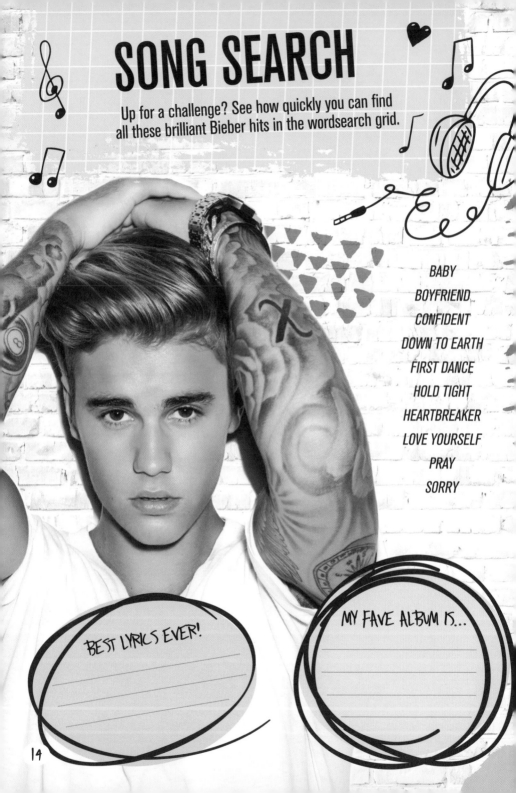

BABY
BOYFRIEND
CONFIDENT
DOWN TO EARTH
FIRST DANCE
HOLD TIGHT
HEARTBREAKER
LOVE YOURSELF
PRAY
SORRY

BEST LYRICS EVER!

MY FAVE ALBUM IS...

14

R	B	J	F	X	R	S	U	H	J	E	M	J	L	I	A	F	E	F	V
V	M	X	H	B	K	V	V	U	B	L	C	O	O	H	V	K	Z	F	Y
W	K	V	J	T	J	A	U	W	H	W	V	N	Z	Q	K	V	K	K	Z
J	B	D	Y	F	M	A	H	R	C	E	D	M	A	E	K	W	N	F	A
A	F	U	R	G	K	V	W	W	Y	W	N	S	V	D	P	J	M	P	D
L	K	W	O	W	M	U	I	O	W	P	E	G	C	L	T	N	A	L	P
N	H	P	Z	L	B	B	U	P	Y	R	I	C	E	J	E	S	O	I	S
D	E	Y	L	M	Q	R	M	E	R	C	R	A	C	D	E	Q	R	H	A
M	A	E	C	N	S	L	E	T	Y	F	F	Y	I	Y	K	A	F	I	A
A	R	V	I	E	K	B	M	I	W	Q	Y	Z	F	E	C	R	F	M	F
N	T	R	L	U	E	H	Z	B	W	H	O	L	D	T	I	G	H	T	F
P	B	F	F	O	R	U	N	B	K	Z	B	S	J	E	F	O	N	K	N
C	R	L	J	B	G	V	V	A	A	P	H	E	Z	B	I	E	C	T	P
K	E	Z	V	H	P	X	W	B	X	Y	R	I	M	O	D	B	Q	J	R
M	A	I	M	Z	V	R	P	Y	K	L	J	E	X	I	N	P	G	Q	T
G	K	T	G	Z	M	S	T	K	K	G	F	S	F	Z	G	K	Y	T	N
F	E	W	X	M	L	G	T	Z	A	O	B	N	O	M	D	N	S	I	J
O	R	K	F	I	M	U	X	Z	I	U	O	L	B	R	N	G	E	W	G
Q	L	A	D	F	H	Z	B	I	L	C	B	J	B	P	R	Q	G	G	W
D	P	I	X	J	B	Q	E	E	G	S	E	T	R	W	Z	Y	S	P	H
I	A	U	N	E	Z	L	A	M	W	S	X	A	D	A	H	N	Q	Y	J
H	T	R	A	E	O	T	N	W	O	D	Y	W	Z	U	M	Y	V	R	X

Answers on page 92

HOW DID YOU DO?

LESS THAN 5 MINS
Wow! It's official, you're a wordsearch whizz!

LESS THAN 10 MINS
Come on, fess up, you wandered off for a sneaky snack while doing it didn't you? Yum!

STILL MISSING A FEW?
We know, we know... it's very hard to concentrate on words when there are so many other amazing things to look at in this book, like the poster on page 94. Maybe finish it later!

GROWING UP

Despite his fame and fortune, home is where the heart is and Justin's family and old friends are still an important part of his life.

THERE'S NO PLACE LIKE HOME

Justin grew up in Stratford, Canada.
The small town was a fun and friendly place to live and where Justin learned to speak French as well as English.

BONJOUR BIEBER!

STRATFORD

EARLY STARTER

The talented JB was experimenting with the piano and guitar before he even started school.
He met his bests buds, Chaz Somers and Ryan Butler, at Jeanne Sauve Catholic School, and they're still his pals today.

SCHOOL RULES

Teachers remember Justin as a leader. If he behaved the whole class behaved, but if he got into mischief, then so did everyone else! JB worked hard to pass all his exams though and finished high school to make his mum happy. Awww!

FAMILY MATTERS

Justin's dad, Jeremy, loves music and got JB into rock from a young age, playing him hits by legendary bands, like Guns n Roses. The pair are so close they have even got matching seagull tattoos on their hips.

JB's mum, Pattie Mallette, has been with Justin every single step on his road to stardom. She's now famous in her own right, with millions of Twitter followers and her own book *Nowhere But Up.*

🐦 @pattiemallette

JB's younger brother and sis, Jaxon and Jasmyn, are treated like VIPs wherever they go. Justin is the best big brother ever, letting his siblings get up on stage with him, throwing them amazing birthday parties and even taking Jazmyn to Disneyland to cheer her up, when she broke her arm.

LOOKING GOOD

If you look good you'll feel good, and if you feel good, you'll look even better! Write down your beauty secrets here.

I USE...

- ☐ moisturiser
- ☐ body cream
- ☐ body spray
- ☐ hair dryer
- ☐ straightners
- ☐ perfume
- ☐ shampoo
- ☐ conditioner
- ☐ make-up
- ☐ nail polish

HOW OFTEN DO YOU...

♥	EVERY DAY	TWICE A DAY	ONCE A WEEK	TWICE A WEEK	ONCE A MONTH	NEVER	OTHER
wash your hair							
brush your teeth							
brush your hair							
get a hair cut							
file your nails							

Try out these beauty tips and tricks for the feel-good factor!

RUB TOOTHPASTE ON YOUR SPOTS TO GET RID OF THEM.

DRINK LOTS OF WATER FOR GLOWING SKIN.

PUT TALC ON YOUR HAIR TO STOP IT LOOKING GREASY.

COMB MAYONNAISE THROUGH WET HAIR FOR GLOSSY LOCKS. (WASH OUT AFTERWARDS!)

SOAK YOUR FINGERS IN OLIVE OIL TO SOFTEN YOUR CUTICLES.

ADD YOUR OWN BEAUTY TIPS BELOW!

19

SPOT IT

Can you spot 5 differences between
these 2 pics of JB?

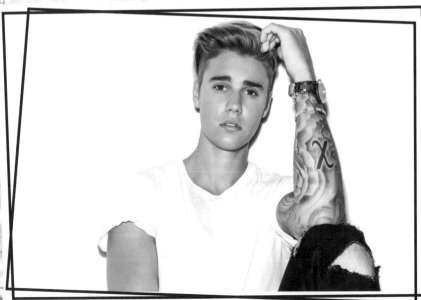

TOO EASY?

Try and find 10 between these 2 pics, too!

Answers on page 92

21

OODLES OF DOODLES

TURN THESE SQUIGGLES
INTO SOMETHING ELSE.

WHAT DO YOU
THINK JB IS
DREAMING OF?

BFF

It takes all sorts of qualities to make the perfect friend. Fill in this page to show what you rate in a mate.

WHO IS YOUR....

best mate _____

kindest pal _____

funniest friend _____

oldest friend _____

WHICH OF YOUR FRIENDS IS THE...

best dancer _____

most organised _____

best shopper _____

most scatterbrained _____

STICK SELFIES OR DRAW PICS OF YOUR FRIENDS HERE.

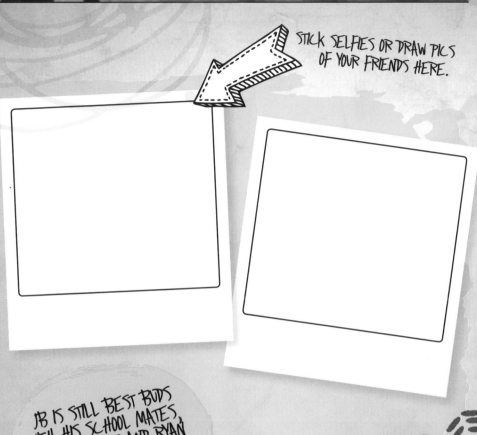

JB IS STILL BEST BUDS WITH HIS SCHOOL MATES, CHAZ SOMERS AND RYAN BUTLER. BUT ALSO HAS NEW CELEB PALS, LIKE ED SHEERAN.

DREAM BIG

Justin dreamt of becoming a music star when he was just a little boy and worked hard to turn his dream into reality. Use the space below to write about your dreams.

MY DREAM...

job _____

holiday _____

outfit _____

day _____

meal _____

WHAT WOULD YOUR DREAM HOME BE LIKE?

☐ millionaire's mansion

☐ castle

☐ beach house

☐ city flat

☐ country ranch

☐ yacht

☐ caravan

WHAT DO YOUR DREAMS MEAN?

FALLING DREAMS

If you dream you are falling, from the sky, down a hole or off a cliff, it can mean you feel out of control. Try to work out what area of your life you need to take control of, and what you can do about it, and these dreams will stop.

FLYING DREAMS

If you dream you are flying it means you feel confident and secure about your life and in control. If you dream you are flying too high it can mean you are concerned how your success might change your life.

BEING NAKED DREAMS

Ever dream you've forgotten to put your clothes on? It usually means you're feeling a bit worried about something. It can also mean you are trying to hide your true self.

WHAT DO YOU DREAM ABOUT MOST?

☐ school   ☐ ghosts

☐ celebs   ☐ films

☐ friends   ☐ family

27

THE BIEBER BREAKTHROUGH

JB's road to success was a long and hard one, with lots of bumps along the way. But he never gave up!

IF AT FIRST YOU DON'T SUCCEED...

Justin failed to win his first talent competition in his home town of Stratford but, never one to give up, he took his music to the streets and busked every weekend, entertaining the locals as they passed him by.

THE FIRST TIME JUSTIN WENT ON A PLANE WAS WHEN HE VISITED HIS SOON-TO-BE MANAGER, SCOOTER BRAUN, IN ATLANTA.

BELIEVE

YOUNG TALENT

Justin's mum, Pattie, posted vids of JB on YouTube when he was young. As the years passed, he gained more and more fans and the music industry started to take an interest in the cute Canadian with a big voice.

MUSIC MAKERS

Scooter Braun came across Justin's videos on YouTube and invited Justin to visit him in Atlanta, where he introduced JB to the talented music coach, Mama Jan, and pop sensation, Usher.

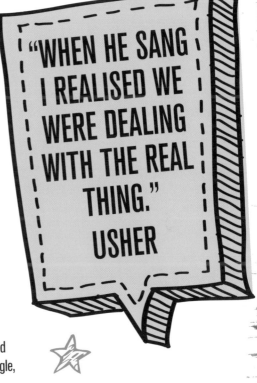

> "WHEN HE SANG I REALISED WE WERE DEALING WITH THE REAL THING."
> USHER

BIG BREAK

Usher helped Justin get a record deal and Justin quickly set to work on his first single, *One Time,* and debut album, *My World.*

HIT AFTER HIT

Justin was bursting with music and lyrics and quickly wrote song after song. *Never Say Never* and *Under the Mistletoe* were released in 2011, both topping the charts in the US and Canada. Next came *Believe* in 2012, *Journals* in 2013 and the best-selling *Purpose* in 2015.

BACKSTAGE
PASS

Help Justin make it through
the maze to perform on stage!

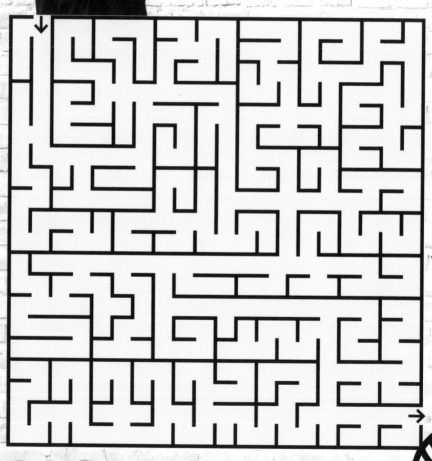

NOTE IT

How quickly can you count up all the different kinds of music notes below?

THE WRITE STUFF

The way you write can reveal a lot about the kind of person you are. Take a look at JB's signature below and what it tells us about him.

LARGE CAPITAL LETTERS DEMONSTRATES CONFIDENCE.

AN UPWARD SLANT MEANS AMBITION.

EASY-TO-READ LETTERS SIGNIFY AN OPEN PERSON.

NO UNDERLINE MEANS JB IS HAPPY TO LET HIS ACHIEVEMENTS SPEAK FOR THEMSELVES.

NOW PRACTISE YOUR OWN SIGNATURE
IN THE SPACE BELOW AND DISCOVER
WHAT IT SAYS ABOUT YOU.

EASY-TO-READ LETTERS – quick mind and mental agility
HARD-TO-READ LETTERS – straightforward person
EASY-TO-READ FIRST NAME BUT HARD-TO-READ LAST NAME
– places importance on personal accomplishments
NO UNDERLINE – prefers to let personal achievements speak
for themselves
UNDERLINE – sense of self importance
CLOSING FLICK OR LINE AT END – drive and determination
SHARP LINES – impatient and aggressive
UPWARD SLOPE – sense of ambition, a tendency
to look towards the future
DOWNWARD SLOPE – pessimistic and cautious
RISING UP ONLY TOWARDS THE END – sense of optimism
SLANT TOWARDS THE RIGHT – ambitious
NO SLANT – balanced
NICKNAME – independent and confident
in own abilities

INITIALS ONLY – private person
NO DOT ON 'I' – reluctant to dwell on small details,
a bigger picture person
OPEN 'O'OR 'A' – collaborative nature, desire
to share ideas
PRONOUNCED CAPITAL LETTERS – confident, strong
sense of self-worth, perhaps arrogant
NO SURNAME – relaxed approach to life
FULL STOP – strong character
STRAIGHT LETTERS – precise and meticulous attention
to detail
SCRIBBLED – sharp intelligence and a busy, very
hectic lifestyle
LARGE, SWOOPING LETTERS – extrovert and confident
HIGHLY STYLIZED – creative flair, likes to make
a statement
LARGE FIRST LETTER – strives to make presence felt

TALENT SPOTTING

JB was super-duper talented from a teeny-tiny age. While not everyone can hope for his amazing musical ability, everyone does have a talent. What's yours?

MY TALENT IS...

_____

BUT I CAN ALSO...

1 _____

2 _____

3 _____

TALENTS I AM STILL WORKING ON ARE...

MY SILLIEST, SECRET TALENT IS...

MY MOST TALENTED FRIEND IS...

THE TALENT I WOULD MOST LOVE TO HAVE IS...

JB TAUGHT HIMSELF TO PLAY MUSICAL INSTRUMENTS BEFORE HE EVEN STARTED SCHOOL!

DOODLE TIME

DOODLE SOME COOL DESIGNS ON THESE TEES.

TURN THESE SQUIGGLES INTO SOME STYLISH ACCESSORIES.

A JB concert.

JUSTIN'S TRADEMARK LOOK IS A PAIR OF SLOUCHY JEANS, TEAMED WITH A COOL TEE OR VEST, TOPPED OFF WITH A BASEBALL CAP!

Shopping with your pals.

A party with JB.

SUPERFUN SUDOKU

Draw some emoticons and music notes
into the grids to complete the puzzles.

THERE CAN ONLY BE
ONE OF EACH EMOTICON
IN EACH COLUMN, ROW
AND TWO-BY-TWO
SQUARE.

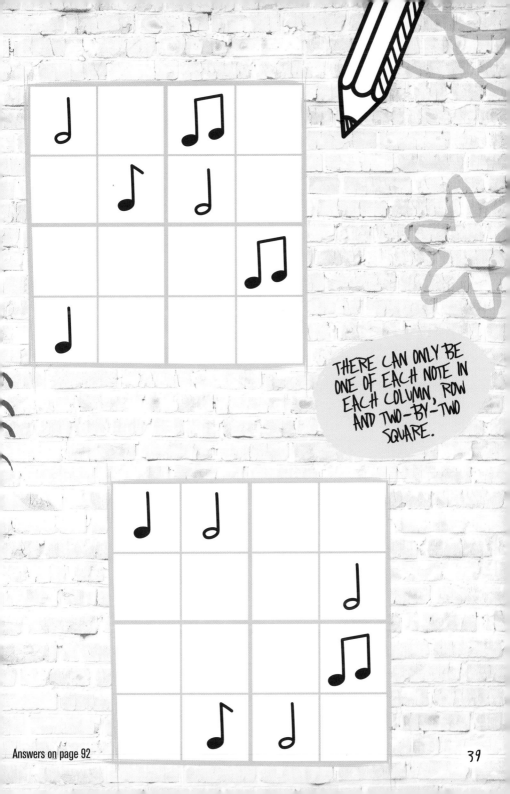

THERE CAN ONLY BE ONE OF EACH NOTE IN EACH COLUMN, ROW AND TWO-BY-TWO SQUARE.

WEAR IT WELL

Fill in the page with all
your fashion faves!

TICK THE ITEMS YOU LOVE TO WEAR AND PUT A X NEXT TO THOSE YOU DON'T!

- [ ] jeans
- [ ] dress
- [ ] maxi skirt
- [ ] trousers

- [ ] shorts
- [ ] short skirt
- [ ] t-shirt
- [ ] culottes

- [ ] jumper
- [ ] jacket
- [ ] waistcoat

MY FAVOURITE CELEBRITY STYLE IS...

_____

MY FAVE SHOP IS...

_____

MY FAVE OUTFIT IS...

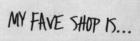

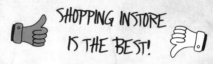
👍 I LOVE TO SHOP ONLINE! 👎

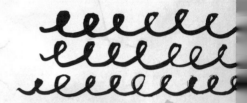
👍 SHOPPING IN STORE IS THE BEST! 👎

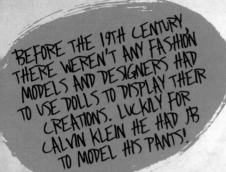
BEFORE THE 19TH CENTURY, THERE WEREN'T ANY FASHION MODELS AND DESIGNERS HAD TO USE DOLLS TO DISPLAY THEIR CREATIONS. LUCKILY FOR CALVIN KLEIN HE HAD JB TO MODEL HIS PANTS!

GOING TO SEE JB IN CONCERT THIS YEAR? CHECK OUT THESE NIFTY TIPS AND TRICKS ON HOW TO ROCK YOUR LOOK!

Key items for a festival are a pair of frayed, faded shorts and wellies.

Team these with a cool t-shirt, with an even cooler slogan, and you'll look the part.

Denim or leather jackets are great for outerwear, but for a more boho look, try a waistcoat.

Accessorize with jewellery and a cute hat.

Don't forget your shades!

BIEBER FASHION

Not content with worldwide domination on the music scene, Justin is trending in fashion too, with a modelling contract for Calvin Klein and appearances in men's style mag *GQ*!

JB LOVES...

bomber jackets

beanies

caps

vests

trainers

shades

bling

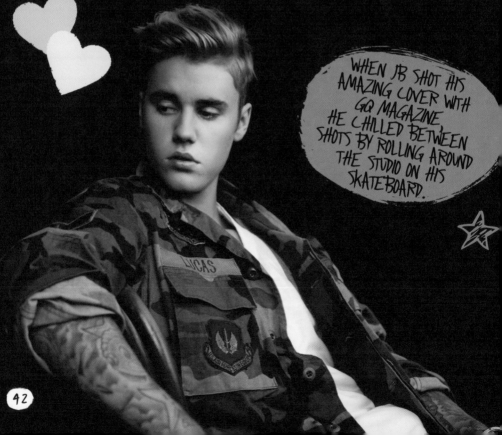

WHEN JB SHOT HIS AMAZING COVER WITH GQ MAGAZINE, HE CHILLED BETWEEN SHOTS BY ROLLING AROUND THE STUDIO ON HIS SKATEBOARD.

STAR STYLE

Number these outfits from 1 (best) to 4 (worst) to rate JB's style.

classic tee

nice shoes

rocking it

urban cool

TOO COOL  FOR SCHOOL

When Justin hit the big time, he didn't have time for school and had to have a private tutor, which he loved. He missed his buddies though. What do you love/hate about your school?

name of your school _____

best subject _____

fave teacher _____

worst teacher _____

most amazing thing you've learned this year _____

_____

IF YOU WERE A TEACHER WHAT WOULD YOU TEACH AND WHY?

JUSTIN LOVED MUSIC AND SPORTS THE MOST AT SCHOOL!

_____

_____

_____

_____

I EAT...

☐ school dinners

☐ packed lunch

school uniform colour _____

best bit about it _____

worst bit about it _____

DESIGN THE PERFECT
SCHOOL UNIFORM HERE.

DON'T FORGET
YOUR SCHOOL
BAG!

WORD UP!

Cross out every letter that appears
three times to reveal JB's fave type of food!

K B I Q M F D X V O K T B Q M F D
X A V O K B Q L M F D X I V A O N

_ _ _ _ _ _ _ _ _ _ _

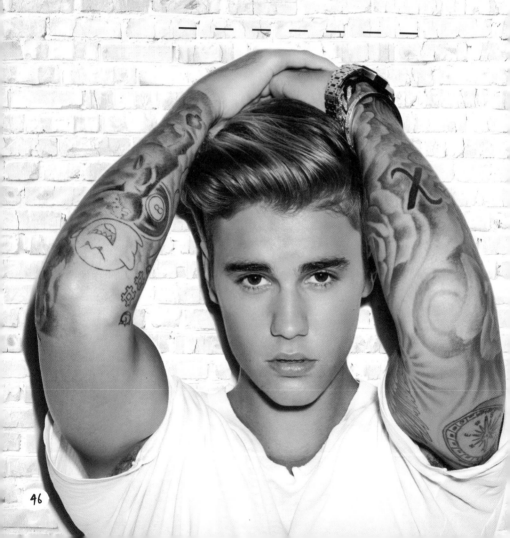

Can you work out the riddles below in less than three mins?

1   If I don't share it, I have it. If I share it, I don't have it. What is it?

_____

2   What travels around but stays in one spot?

_____

3   What occurs once in a minute, twice in a moment but never in a thousand years?

_____

Can you work out the phrases behind these puzzles?

1   HEAD
    HEELS

3   SECRET ←

2   ALL   ALL
       WORLD
    ALL   ALL

1 _____

2 _____

3 _____

How many words can you make from this sentence:

Justin Bieber is amazing!

_____   _____   _____

_____   _____   _____

_____   _____   _____

_____

HAPPY HOLS

JB has travelled the world thanks
to his music, and created some amazing
memories that will last a lifetime.
What are your holiday highs and lows?

BEST HOLIDAY MEMORY EVER...

_____

_____

WORST HOLIDAY

MEMORY...   _____

_____

MY FAVE KIND OF HOLIDAY IS...

☐ camping   ☐ sightseeing

☐ beach   ☐ diving

☐ safari   ☐ ski-ing

☐ activity

Put a cross to mark where in the
world you'd like to visit most!

IF I COULD GO ON HOLIDAY WITH
ANYONE I WOULD GO WITH...

FAVE BOOK FOR HOLIDAY
READING...

FAVE MUSIC TO CHILL
OUT TO ON THE BEACH...

HOLIDAY HOTSPOTS

Even rock stars need to kick back and relax sometimes and JB loves to holiday with friends and family all over the world.

HOLIDAY HAIR

JB recently took his friend, Hailey Baldwin, to St Barts, where the cute couple chilled out on the beach, soaked up the sun and JB even let Hailey talk him into getting a new holiday hairstyle.

DISNEY DREAM

It's no secret that JB loves Disneyland. He busked as a young boy to earn enough money to go and, when his little sis broke her arm, he took her to the Magic Kingdom to cheer her up.

TRAVEL BUDDIES

Bieber's trip to Bora Bora caused a stir when he was snapped with British beauty vlogger, Jayde Pierce. Jayde posted loads of IG shots of her in beautiful blue waters and said it was her first time on a jet ski!

@jaydepierce

HOLIDAY VIDS

JB loves sharing his holiday memories with his fans and posted videos of himself in Italy on IG, discussing what delicious Italian food he was going to tuck into for lunch. Yum!

DOODLY DO!

As JB always tells us, you've got to *Believe* to make it happen! Doodle some of your holiday dreams into the space below.

TURN THESE SQUIGGLES INTO SOME DREAM WAVES TO SURF ON!

DOODLE WHERE YOU'D LIKE TO GO ON YOUR NEXT HOLIDAY.

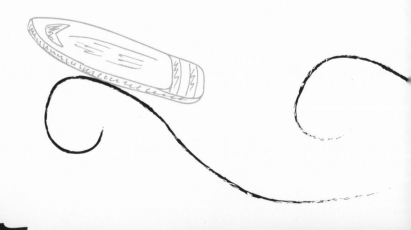

SQUIGGLE SOME SNOWY MOUNTAINS TO SKI DOWN.

DOODLE SOME ICE CREAM
ONTO THESE CONES.

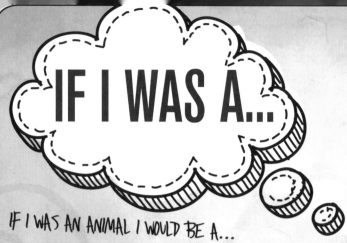

IF I WAS A...

Ever wondered what it would be like to be something completely different? What would you be?

IF I WAS AN ANIMAL I WOULD BE A...

_____

IF I WAS A FISH I WOULD BE A...

_____

IF I WAS A COLOUR I WOULD BE...

_____

IF I WAS A CHOCOLATE
BAR I WOULD BE A...   _____

IF I WAS A NUMBER I WOULD BE NUMBER...

_____

IF I WAS A POP STAR
I WOULD BE JUST LIKE... _____

IF I WAS A MOVIE STAR
I WOULD BE JUST LIKE...

IF I WAS A PLANET I WOULD BE...

_____

IF I WAS AN ICE-CREAM FLAVOUR
I WOULD TASTE LIKE..._____

IF I WAS A FLOWER I WOULD BE A...

_____

IF I COULD BE ANYONE IN THE WORLD I WOULD BE...

_____

IF I COULD GIVE MYSELF
A NEW NAME IT WOULD BE...

_____

IF JUSTIN HADN'T
BECOME A MUSIC
LEGEND HE MIGHT HAVE
BEEN A MUSIC TEACHER
OR PLAYED ICE HOCKEY!

DOODLE TO THE BEAT

CLOSE YOUR EYES, CRANK UP YOUR FAVE JB TUNE AND DOODLE WHATEVER COMES INTO YOUR HEAD!

MUSIC MAKER

Take the time to truly listen to JB's lyrics and you'll realize how magical his music is. But what is Justin's winning formula?

JB IS THE YOUNGEST ARTIST TO TOP THE US BILLBOARD TOP 100.

COLLABS

Ed Sheeran, Jack U, Drake, Nicki Minaj, Big Sean and Skrillex are just a few of the amazing peeps JB has collabed with. His skill of picking the perfect partner for his tunes helps blend hip-hop, rap, R&B and smooth vocals to create music we can't stop listening to.

MEANING

There's always a story behind JB's tunes and he admitted three of his songs off the *Purpose* album are about his ex, Selina Gomez. *Sorry*, *What Do You Mean?* and *Mark My Words* all tell the tale of his relationship with his first love and their painful break up.

"I WROTE *BELIEVE* FOR MY FANS AND HOW THEY INSPIRED ME. IT MEANS A LOT."

IT TOOK ONLY FIVE WEEKS FOR *PURPOSE* TO SELL A MILLION COPIES.

ALL NIGHTER!

Staying up all night, listening to JB's music and swapping secrets with your besties... what could be better than a Justin Bieber sleepover party!

WHAT YOU NEED...

- [ ] snacks
- [ ] music
- [ ] sleeping bag
- [ ] pillow
- [ ] torch
- [ ] PJs
- [ ] new make-up and accessories to try out

INVITE LIST

_____   _____

_____   _____

_____   _____

_____   _____

SNACKS SHOPPING LIST

JB MUSIC PLAYLIST

1 _____

2 _____

3 _____

4 _____

5 _____

6 _____

7 _____

8 _____

9 _____

10 _____

TIP! In the summer time, take your sleepover outdoors and camp out under the stars in a tent. Decorate your garden with some fairy lights but keep an eye out for creepy crawlies!

PUZZLE TIME

Can you fit all these JB songs
in the wordgrid opposite?

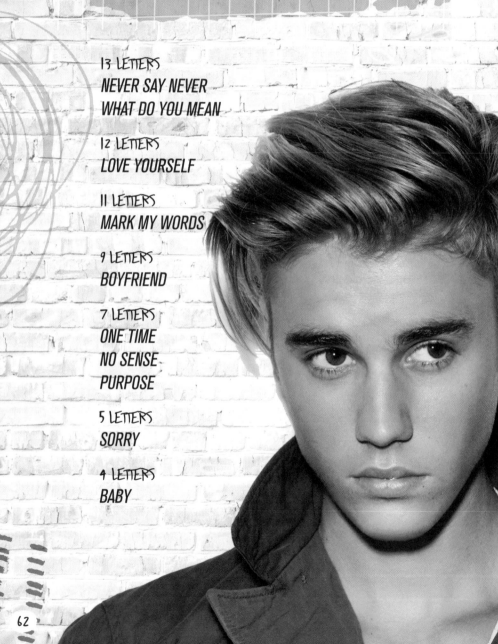

13 LETTERS
NEVER SAY NEVER
WHAT DO YOU MEAN

12 LETTERS
LOVE YOURSELF

11 LETTERS
MARK MY WORDS

9 LETTERS
BOYFRIEND

7 LETTERS
ONE TIME
NO SENSE
PURPOSE

5 LETTERS
SORRY

4 LETTERS
BABY

B O Y F R I E N D

Answers on page 92

MUSIC & ME

Fill this page with all your fave things about JB's music!

MY FAVE JB ALBUM IS...

_____

MY FAVE JB VIDEO IS...

_____

MY FAVE BIEBER SONG TO DANCE TO IS...

_____

MY FAVE BIEBER LYRICS ARE IN...

WRITE THEM HERE _____

_____
_____
_____
_____

5 JB SONGS YOU KNOW ALL THE WORDS TO!

1 _____

2 _____

3 _____

4 _____

5 _____

BEST JB SONG TO SING IN THE SHOWER IS...

_____

64

BEYOND THE HYPE

Read on to discover what Justin likes to get up to when he can steal a bit of 'me time'!

WHEELY FUN

JB loves to cruise around on his skateboard. He can do some nifty tricks too and loves nothing more than skating with his famous pals, like Lil' Wayne.

ICE ICE BABY

JB loves ice hockey and hits the ice whenever he can. His fave team is the Toronto Maple Leafs, from his native Canada, and one of Justin's childhood dreams came true when he got to hang out with them on the ice.

SHOOTING HOOPS

When Justin's in LA he can be found courtside cheering on his fave basketball team, the LA Lakers. So, if you're ever in LA, head to the Staples Center where the team plays its home games and you might spot Bieber on the sidelines.

VROOM VROOM

A Range Rover, Lamborghini, Porsche and Ferrari are just a few of the cars motorhead JB has parked in his garage. That doesn't stop Justin from carpooling though. Check out his hilarious *Carpool Karaoke* sketches with James Corden on YouTube.

DOWNTIME

What do you love to do more than anything else (apart from listening to JB's music that is!)? Fill this page with all your fave hobbies and perfect pastimes.

MY MOST FAVE THING TO DO EVER IS...

_____

I ♥ TO...

- [ ] read
- [ ] listen to music
- [ ] gossip
- [ ] sing

- [ ] chill
- [ ] draw
- [ ] dance
- [ ] cook

- [ ] write
- [ ] watch tv

AFTER SCHOOL
I MOSTLY LIKE TO...

_____

_____

ON THE WEEKENDS
I LOVE TO...

_____

_____

I WOULD ♥ TO TRY...

- [ ] sky diving
- [ ] bungee jumping
- [ ] flying
- [ ] deep-sea diving
- [ ] horse riding
- [ ] space travel

FILL IN THE WEEKLY DIARY BELOW WITH YOUR REGULAR ACTIVITIES.

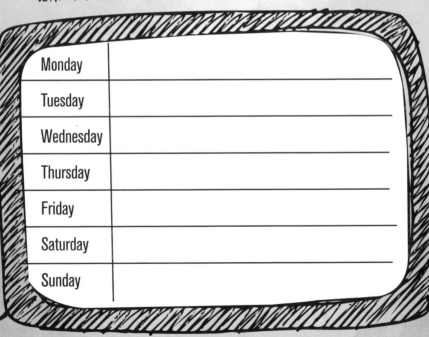

Monday	
Tuesday	
Wednesday	
Thursday	
Friday	
Saturday	
Sunday	

MISSING LYRICS

Fill in the gaps to finish off JB's biggest hits!

SORRY

You gotta go and get angry at all of my _____

You know I try but _____ with apologies

I hope I don't run out of time. Could someone call a _____?

'Cause I just need one more _____ at forgiveness

BOYFRIEND

If I was your _____, I'd never let you go

Keep you on my arm girl, you'd never be _____

I can be a _____, anything you want

If I was your boyfriend, I'd never let you go, I'd never let you _____

LOVE YOURSELF

My mama don't like you and she likes _____

And I never like to _____ that I was wrong

And I've been so _____ up in my job

Didn't see what's going _____

But now I _____

I'm better _____ on my own

BEAUTY AND A BEAT

We gonna _____ like it's 3012 tonight
I wanna show you all the _____ things in life
So just forget about the_____, we're young tonight
I'm coming for ya, I'm _____ for ya

Answers on page 92

71

BIEB-RILLIANT BIRTHDAYS

Make sure you're all set for your next birthday with some party preparation.

PRESENT WISHLIST! I WANT...

1 _____

2 _____

3 _____

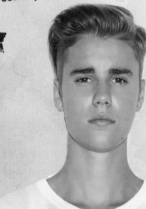

PARTY INVITE GUEST LIST...

_____

_____

_____

_____

_____

JUSTIN WAS BORN 1 MARCH 1994 AND IS A PISCES, WHO ARE DETERMINED, BUT SENSITIVE.

TYPE OF PARTY...

- [ ] disco
- [ ] sleepover
- [ ] other _____

- [ ] bowling
- [ ] cinema

- [ ] paintballing
- [ ] pizza

DOODLE YOUR DREAM
PARTY OUTFIT HERE.

JUSTIN CELEBRATED
HIS 22ND BIRTHDAY WITH
A GROUP OF PALS IN SOME
AMAZING ICE-COVERED
CAVES, IN THE CANADIAN
WILDERNESS.

DOODLE DO

DOODLE YOUR OWN COVER ARTWORK FOR SOME OF JUSTIN'S ALBUMS.

PURPOSE

BELIEVE

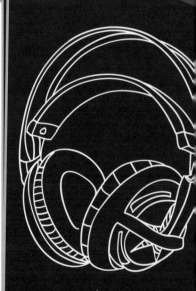

MY WORLD

Under the Mistletoe

Use this space to doodle some illustrations
for your fave JB song and what it means to you.

QUIZ

Put your Belieber know-how to the test
with our bumper Bieber quiz!

1 HOW OLD WAS JUSTIN WHEN HIS MUM STARTED
UPLOADING HIS MUSIC ONTO YOUTUBE?

☐ 8
☐ 12
☐ 16

2 WHAT IS THE NAME
OF JUSTIN'S HOME TOWN?

☐ Toronto
☐ Vancouver
☐ Stratford

3 WHAT ARE THE NAMES
OF JB'S SIBLINGS?

☐ Jaxon and Jasmyn
☐ Jerry and Joanie
☐ Jimmy and Jessie

4 WHICH OF THESE POP STARS
HAS JUSTIN NOT COLLABED WITH?

☐ Adam Levine
☐ Ed Sheeran
☐ Usher

5 WHICH OF THESE SONGS WAS JUSTIN'S FIRST HIT?

☐ Boyfriend   ☐ One Time   ☐ Baby

Answers on page 92

6 WHICH OF THESE IS JB'S FAVE FOOD?

☐ spag bol   ☐ burger   ☑ nachos

7 WHICH MONTH IS JUSTIN'S BIRTHDAY IN?

☐ January

☐ March

☐ September

8 WHICH OF THESE IS NOT A JUSTIN BIEBER SONG?

☐ Somebody to Love

☐ Love Yourself

☐ Love Hurts

9 WHICH KIND OF VEHICLES DOES JB OWN A LOT OF?

☐ helicopters

☐ trucks

☐ cars

10 WHEN JUSTIN WRITES HIS AMAZING SONGS, WHICH HAND DOES HE WRITE WITH?

☐ left

☐ right

☐ both

77

January

1 ....
2 ....
3 ....
4 ....
5 ....
6 ....
7 ....
8 ....
9 ....
10 ....
11 ....
12 ....
13 ....
14 ....
15 ....
16 ....
17 ....
18 ....
19 ....
20 ....
21 ....
22 ....
23 ....
24 ....
25 ....
26 ....
27 ....
28 ....
29 ....
30 ....
31 ....

February

1 ....
2 ....
3 ....
4 ....
5 ....
6 ....
7 ....
8 ....
9 ....
10 ....
11 ....
12 ....
13 ....
14 ....
15 ....
16 ....
17 ....
18 ....
19 ....
20 ....
21 ....
22 ....
23 ....
24 ....
25 ....
26 ....
27 ....
28 ....
29 ....

March

1 ....
2 ....
3 ....
4 ....
5 ....
6 ....
7 ....
8 ....
9 ....
10 ....
11 ....
12 ....
13 ....
14 ....
15 ....
16 ....
17 ....
18 ....
19 ....
20 ....
21 ....
22 ....
23 ....
24 ....
25 ....
26 ....
27 ....
28 ....
29 ....
30 ....
31 ....

April

1 ....
2 ....
3 ....
4 ....
5 ....
6 ....
7 ....
8 ....
9 ....
10 ....
11 ....
12 ....
13 ....
14 ....
15 ....
16 ....
17 ....
18 ....
19 ....
20 ....
21 ....
22 ....
23 ....
24 ....
25 ....
26 ....
27 ....
28 ....
29 ....
30 ....

May

1 ....
2 ....
3 ....
4 ....
5 ....
6 ....
7 ....
8 ....
9 ....
10 ....
11 ....
12 ....
13 ....
14 ....
15 ....
16 ....
17 ....
18 ....
19 ....
20 ....
21 ....
22 ....
23 ....
24 ....
25 ....
26 ....
27 ....
28 ....
29 ....
30 ....
31 ....

June

1 ....
2 ....
3 ....
4 ....
5 ....
6 ....
7 ....
8 ....
9 ....
10 ....
11 ....
12 ....
13 ....
14 ....
15 ....
16 ....
17 ....
18 ....
19 ....
20 ....
21 ....
22 ....
23 ....
24 ....
25 ....
26 ....
27 ....
28 ....
29 ....
30 ....

July

1 ....
2 ....
3 ....
4 ....
5 ....
6 ....
7 ....
8 ....
9 ....
10 ....
11 ....
12 ....
13 ....
14 ....
15 ....
16 ....
17 ....
18 ....
19 ....
20 ....
21 ....
22 ....
23 ....
24 ....
25 ....
26 ....
27 ....
28 ....
29 ....
30 ....
31 ....

August

1 ....
2 ....
3 ....
4 ....
5 ....
6 ....
7 ....
8 ....
9 ....
10 ....
11 ....
12 ....
13 ....
14 ....
15 ....
16 ....
17 ....
18 ....
19 ....
20 ....
21 ....
22 ....
23 ....
24 ....
25 ....
26 ....
27 ....
28 ....
29 ....
30 ....
31 ....

September

1
2
3
4
5
6
7
8
9
10
11
12
13
14
15
16
17
18
19
20
21
22
23
24
25
26
27
28
29
30

October

1
2
3
4
5
6
7
8
9
10
11
12
13
14
15
16
17
18
19
20
21
22
23
24
25
26
27
28
29
30
31

November

1 ....
2 ....
3 ....
4 ....
5 ....
6 ....
7 ....
8 ....
9 ....
10 ....
11 ....
12 ....
13 ....
14 ....
15 ....
16 ....
17 ....
18 ....
19 ....
20 ....
21 ....
22 ....
23 ....
24 ....
25 ....
26 ....
27 ....
28 ....
29 ....
30 ....

December

1 ....
2 ....
3 ....
4 ....
5 ....
6 ....
7 ....
8 ....
9 ....
10 ....
11 ....
12 ....
13 ....
14 ....
15 ....
16 ....
17 ....
18 ....
19 ....
20 ....
21 ....
22 ....
23 ....
24 ....
25 ....
26 ....
27 ....
28 ....
29 ....
30 ....
31 ....

BIRTHDAY REMINDERS!

name _____

birthday _____

age _____

star sign _____

perfect present _____

name _____

birthday _____

age _____

star sign _____

perfect present _____

name _____

birthday _____

age _____

star sign _____

perfect present _____

name _____

birthday _____

age _____

star sign _____

perfect present _____

Make sure you remember all your family
and friends' birthdays by writing them here.

name _____

birthday _____

age _____

star sign _____

perfect present _____

name _____

birthday _____

age _____

star sign _____

perfect present _____

name _____

birthday _____

age _____

star sign _____

perfect present _____

name _____

birthday _____

age _____

star sign _____

perfect present _____

ANSWERS

p11 DO YOU KNOW JUSTIN?
ice hockey, spag bol, purple

p15 SONG SEARCH

```
R B J F X R S U H J E M J L I A F E F V
V M X H B K V V U B L C O H V K Z F Y
W K V J T J A U W N V Z Q K V K X A
J B D Y F M A H R C E D M A E K W N F A
A F U R G K V W W W N S V D P J M P D
L K W O W M U I O W P E G C L T N A L P
N R P Z L B B U P Y R I C E J E S O I S
D E Y L M Q R M E R C R A C D E Q R H A
M A E C N S L E T Y F F Y I Y K A F I A
A R V I E K B M I W Q Y Z F E C R F M E
N T R L U E H Z B W H O L D T I G H T F
P B F F D R U N B J S J E F O N K N
C R L J B G V V A A P H E Z B I E C T
K E Z V H P X W B X Y R I M O D B Q J
M A I M Z V R P Y K L J E X I N P G Q O
G K T G Z M S T K K G F S F Z G G X Y D
F E W X M L G T Z A O B N D M N S I J
O R K F I M U X Z I U O L B R N G E W G
Q L A D F T J Z B I L C B J E R P Q O G
D P I X J B Q E E G S E T R W Z Y S P
I A U N E Z L A M W S X A D A H N Q Y J
H T R A E O T N W O D Y W Z U M Y V R X
```

p30 BACKSTAGE PASS

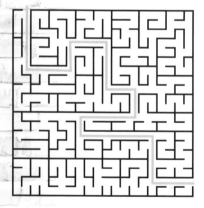

p31 NOTE IT

♩ 20   ♪ 9

♫ 5   ♩ 10

p20 SPOT IT

p38 SUPERFUN SUDOKU

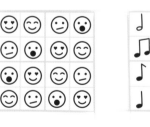

92

p46 WORD UP

ITALIAN

1. a secret
2. a stamp
3. the letter m

1. head over heels
2. all around the world
3. top sercret

Example words
tin, time, bus, just, bat, bin, sing,
sat, jam, sister, mat, but, get, tab,
ring, jabbering, jabber, submarine,
babe, size, bugbear, babies, genius,
unite, size, sings, sizings, me, tinier,
unite, zit, jigs, uniting, men, rabbits,
beaming...

p62 PUZZLE TIME

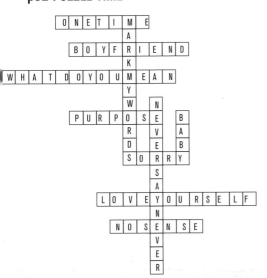

p70 MISSING LYRICS

Sorry
honesty
I don't do to well
referee
shot

Boyfriend
Boyfriend
done
gentleman
you go

Love Yourself
everyone
admit
caught
on
know
sleeping

Beauty and a Beat
party
finer
world
coming

p76 QUIZ

1 = 12
2 = Stratford
3 = Jaxon and Jasmyn
4 = Adam Levine
5 = *One Time*
6 = spag bol
7 = March
8 = *Somebody to Love*
9 = cars
10 = left